E
319.1205

A WISHING WELL Book
Published by Joshua Morris Publishing, Inc.,
355 Riverside Avenue, Westport, CT 06880.
Copyright © 1986 The Five Mile Press Pty. Ltd.
All rights reserved. Printed in Singapore.
ISBN: 0-88705-748-9
10 9 8 7 6 5 4 3 2

It's Much Too Hot!

BOB GRAHAM

WISHING WELL BOOKS®

It's much too hot.
Look at the flowers.

It's too hot for dogs.
Look at Patch's tongue.

And it's too hot for Jenny.
Look at her mop her wet brow.

There is only one place for Patch.

It's cooler in the shade of a tree.

Jenny's feet are hot and sticky.
Look how pink they are.

There is only one thing to
do with feet like that.

There is only one thing to
do with the garden hose.

Jenny feels much cooler.

Her droopy flowers may soon
feel better too.

When Jenny stops watering,
the heat will dry the puddles.

Jenny is looking for things to water.
Patch will find another cool shadow.

He does not like water games.

When the sun goes down . . .

. . . it will be much cooler.

heat

When a liquid becomes a vapor, the heat that causes this change is known as the latent heat of evaporation. When evaporation occurs, the water seems to disappear into the air; however, this is not the case. All matter consists of tiny particles, called molecules. In liquids these molecules are widely separated, but in gases they are even farther apart. When heated, the molecules in water move about rapidly, moving farther and farther apart until they eventually escape as water vapor.

Experiments to try

1. Puddles provide a good example of evaporation. Have your child outline a puddle in chalk and, after about 10 minutes, make another outline to see how much water has evaporated.
2. Have your child place a mixture of water and salt in a saucer and leave it in a sunny place. What is left when the water evaporates?
3. Have your child time how long it takes for a block of ice to melt:
   a. in the sun
   b. in the shade